25 Days of Christmas Bible Verses for Advent

A Christian Devotional & Coloring Journal

written & designed by Shalana Frisby

Get organized for success in your Bible study!
Download your bonus free printables now:

WWW.123JOURNALIT.COM / FREEBIES
SCRIPTURE FLASHCARDS - BIBLE READING PROMPTS - JOURNALING PAGES

More information at: www.123journalit.com

First Printing: October 2018
1 2 3 Journal It Publishing

ISBN-13: 978-1-947209-92-3
25 Days of Bible Verses Series: Christmas Advent Edition

This journal belongs to

_____

_____

How to use this journal:

Find a quiet place and start with prayer asking for guidance.

Write the included daily verses using your preferred bible version.

Dig deeper by filling in the sections on the study notes page.

Journal reflections about life and your additional notes.

Get creative by coloring, doodling, and drawing.

...have fun hiding God's Word in your heart...

Write, Reflect, & Repeat Daily

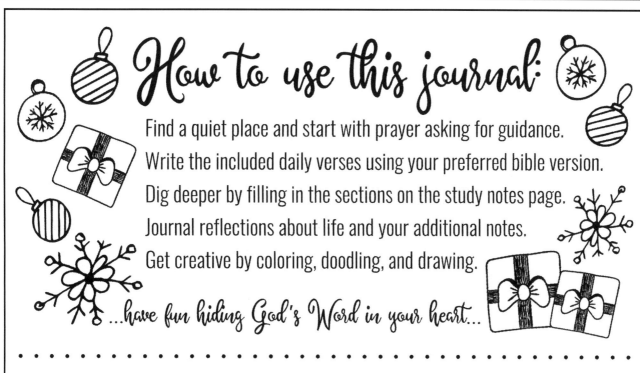

The 25 Bible Verses Featured:

John 1:1-5

Isaiah 7:14

Luke 1:26-28

Luke 1:29-31

Luke 1:32-33

Isaiah 9:6-7

Luke 1:34-35

Luke 1:36-38

Luke 1:41-43

Luke 1:44-45

Luke 1:46-50

Galatians 4:4-5

Luke 1:67-69

Matthew 1:20-22

Luke 2:1-5

Luke 2:6-7

Micah 5:2

Luke 2:8-11

Luke 2:12-16

Matthew 2:1-2

Matthew 2:10-11

Matthew 2:13-14
& Hosea 11:1

Matthew 2:16-18
& Jeremiah 31:15

Matthew 2:19-23

John 3:16-18

PRAY & WRITE TODAY'S VERSE:
John 1:1-5

_____
_____
_____
_____
_____
_____
_____
_____
_____
_____
_____
_____
_____
_____
_____
_____
_____

STUDY NOTES: *what does this scripture mean?*

_____
_____
_____
_____
_____
_____
_____
_____
_____
_____

PRAYER REQUESTS
& praise for answered prayers:

....
....
....
....
....
....
....
....

DIG DEEPER: *how does it apply to my life?*

_____
_____
_____
_____
_____
_____
_____
_____

GIVE THANKS
what I'm grateful for today:

....
....
....
....
....
....
....

REFLECTIONS & NOTES:

PRAY & WRITE TODAY'S VERSE:
Isaiah 7:14

STUDY NOTES: what does this scripture mean?

TODAY'S date: _____

_____
_____
_____
_____
_____
_____
_____
_____
_____
_____
_____

PRAYER REQUESTS
& praise for answered prayers:

....
....
....
....
....
....
....
....

DIG DEEPER: how does it apply to my life?

_____
_____
_____
_____
_____
_____
_____
_____

GIVE THANKS
what I'm grateful for today:

....
....
....
....
....
....
....

REFLECTIONS & NOTES:

PRAY & WRITE TODAY'S VERSE:

Luke 1:26–28

STUDY NOTES: what does this scripture mean?

_____

_____

_____

_____

_____

_____

_____

_____

_____

_____

_____

PRAYER REQUESTS
& praise for answered prayers:

....

....

....

....

....

....

....

....

DIG DEEPER: how does it apply to my life?

_____

_____

_____

_____

_____

_____

_____

_____

_____

_____

GIVE THANKS
what I'm grateful for today:

....

....

....

....

....

....

....

....

REFLECTIONS & NOTES:

PRAY & WRITE TODAY'S VERSE:

Luke 1:29-31

_____
_____
_____
_____
_____
_____
_____
_____
_____
_____
_____

STUDY NOTES: what does this scripture mean?

_____
_____
_____
_____
_____
_____
_____
_____
_____
_____

DIG DEEPER: how does it apply to my life?

_____
_____
_____
_____
_____
_____
_____
_____

TODAY'S date: _____

PRAYER REQUESTS
& praise for answered prayers:

. . . .
. . . .
. . . .
. . . .
. . . .
. . . .
. . . .
. . . .

GIVE THANKS
what I'm grateful for today:

. . . .
. . . .
. . . .
. . . .
. . . .
. . . .
. . . .

REFLECTIONS & NOTES:

PRAY & WRITE TODAY'S VERSE:

Luke 1:32-33

STUDY NOTES: what does this scripture mean?

_____
_____
_____
_____
_____
_____
_____
_____
_____
_____
_____

TODAY'S date: _____

PRAYER REQUESTS
& praise for answered prayers:

....
....
....
....
....
....
....
....

DIG DEEPER: how does it apply to my life?

_____
_____
_____
_____
_____
_____
_____
_____

GIVE THANKS
what I'm grateful for today:

....
....
....
....
....
....
....

REFLECTIONS & NOTES:

_____

_____

_____

_____

_____

_____

_____

_____

_____

_____

_____

_____

_____

_____

_____

_____

_____

_____

_____

PRAY & WRITE TODAY'S VERSE:

Isaiah 9:6-7

STUDY NOTES: what does this scripture mean?

_____
_____
_____
_____
_____
_____
_____
_____
_____
_____
_____

TODAY'S date: _____

PRAYER REQUESTS
& praise for answered prayers:

....
....
....
....
....
....
....
....

DIG DEEPER: how does it apply to my life?

_____
_____
_____
_____
_____
_____

GIVE THANKS
what I'm grateful for today:

....
....
....
....
....
....
....
....

REFLECTIONS & NOTES:

_____

_____

_____

_____

_____

_____

_____

_____

_____

_____

_____

_____

_____

_____

_____

_____

_____

_____

PRAY & WRITE TODAY'S VERSE:

Luke 1:34-35

STUDY NOTES: what does this scripture mean?

_____
_____
_____
_____
_____
_____
_____
_____
_____
_____

DIG DEEPER: how does it apply to my life?

_____
_____
_____
_____
_____
_____
_____
_____

TODAY'S date: _____

PRAYER REQUESTS
& praise for answered prayers:

....
....
....
....
....
....
....
....

GIVE THANKS
what I'm grateful for today:

....
....
....
....
....
....
....

REFLECTIONS & NOTES:

PRAY & WRITE TODAY'S VERSE:

Luke 1:36-38

STUDY NOTES: what does this scripture mean?

_____
_____
_____
_____
_____
_____
_____
_____
_____
_____
_____

DIG DEEPER: how does it apply to my life?

_____
_____
_____
_____
_____
_____
_____

TODAY'S date: _____

PRAYER REQUESTS
& praise for answered prayers:

. . . .
. . . .
. . . .
. . . .
. . . .
. . . .
. . . .
. . . .

GIVE THANKS
what I'm grateful for today:

. . . .
. . . .
. . . .
. . . .
. . . .
. . . .
. . . .

REFLECTIONS & NOTES:

PRAY & WRITE TODAY'S VERSE:

Luke 1:41-43

STUDY NOTES: what does this scripture mean?

_____
_____
_____
_____
_____
_____
_____
_____
_____

DIG DEEPER: how does it apply to my life?

_____
_____
_____
_____
_____
_____
_____
_____

TODAY'S date: _____

PRAYER REQUESTS
& praise for answered prayers:

....
....
....
....
....
....
....
....
....

GIVE THANKS
what I'm grateful for today:

....
....
....
....
....
....
....
....

REFLECTIONS & NOTES:

PRAY & WRITE TODAY'S VERSE:
Luke 1:44–45

STUDY NOTES: what does this scripture mean?

_____
_____
_____
_____
_____
_____
_____
_____
_____
_____

DIG DEEPER: how does it apply to my life?

_____
_____
_____
_____
_____
_____
_____
_____
_____

TODAY'S date: _____

PRAYER REQUESTS
& praise for answered prayers:

....
....
....
....
....
....
....
....

GIVE THANKS
what I'm grateful for today:

....
....
....
....
....
....
....
....

REFLECTIONS & NOTES:

PRAY & WRITE TODAY'S VERSE:
Luke 1:46-50

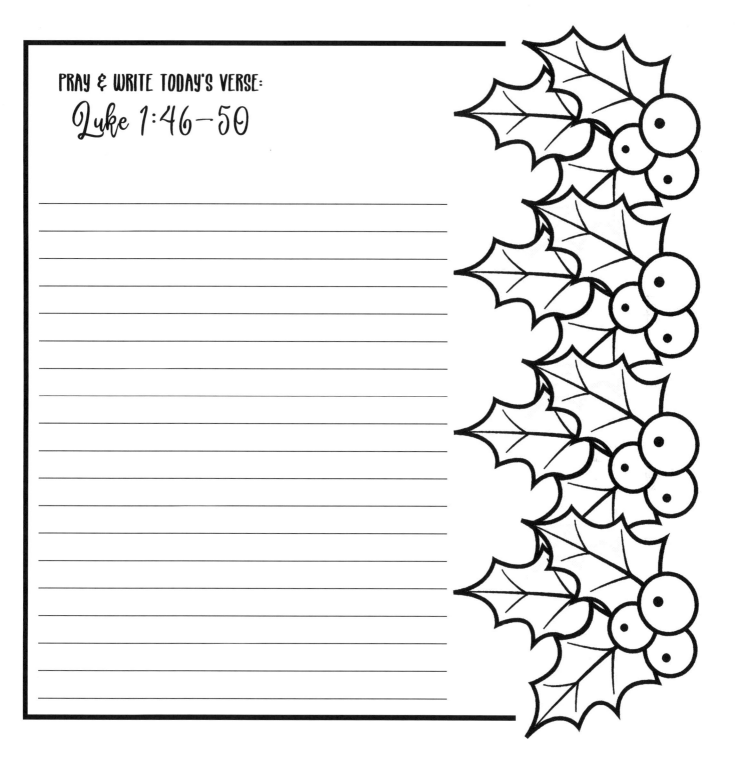

STUDY NOTES: what does this scripture mean?

_____
_____
_____
_____
_____
_____
_____
_____
_____
_____

DIG DEEPER: how does it apply to my life?

_____
_____
_____
_____
_____
_____
_____
_____

TODAY'S date: _____

PRAYER REQUESTS
& praise for answered prayers:

....
....
....
....
....
....
....
....
....

GIVE THANKS
what I'm grateful for today:

....
....
....
....
....
....
....

REFLECTIONS & NOTES:

PRAY & WRITE TODAY'S VERSE:
Galatians 4:4-5

STUDY NOTES: what does this scripture mean?

_____
_____
_____
_____
_____
_____
_____
_____
_____
_____

DIG DEEPER: how does it apply to my life?

_____
_____
_____
_____
_____
_____
_____
_____

TODAY'S date: _____

PRAYER REQUESTS
& praise for answered prayers:

....
....
....
....
....
....
....
....

GIVE THANKS
what I'm grateful for today:

....
....
....
....
....
....
....
....

REFLECTIONS & NOTES:

PRAY & WRITE TODAY'S VERSE:
Luke 1:67-69

STUDY NOTES: *what does this scripture mean?*

_____
_____
_____
_____
_____
_____
_____
_____
_____
_____
_____

TODAY'S *date:* _____

PRAYER REQUESTS
& praise for answered prayers:

....
....
....
....
....
....
....
....
....

DIG DEEPER: *how does it apply to my life?*

_____
_____
_____
_____
_____
_____
_____
_____
_____

GIVE THANKS
what I'm grateful for today:

....
....
....
....
....
....
....
....
....

REFLECTIONS & NOTES:

PRAY & WRITE TODAY'S VERSE:

Matthew 1:20→22

STUDY NOTES: what does this scripture mean?

_____
_____
_____
_____
_____
_____
_____
_____
_____
_____

DIG DEEPER: how does it apply to my life?

_____
_____
_____
_____
_____
_____
_____
_____

TODAY'S date: _____

PRAYER REQUESTS
& praise for answered prayers:

. . . .
. . . .
. . . .
. . . .
. . . .
. . . .
. . . .
. . . .

GIVE THANKS
what I'm grateful for today:

. . . .
. . . .
. . . .
. . . .
. . . .
. . . .
. . . .

REFLECTIONS & NOTES:

PRAY & WRITE TODAY'S VERSE:

Luke 2:1-5

STUDY NOTES: what does this scripture mean?

_____
_____
_____
_____
_____
_____
_____
_____
_____
_____

DIG DEEPER: how does it apply to my life?

_____
_____
_____
_____
_____
_____
_____
_____
_____

TODAY'S date: _____

PRAYER REQUESTS
& praise for answered prayers:

. . . .
. . . .
. . . .
. . . .
. . . .
. . . .
. . . .
. . . .

GIVE THANKS
what I'm grateful for today:

. . . .
. . . .
. . . .
. . . .
. . . .
. . . .
. . . .
. . . .

REFLECTIONS & NOTES:

PRAY & WRITE TODAY'S VERSE:

Luke 2:6-7

STUDY NOTES: what does this scripture mean?

TODAY'S date: _____

PRAYER REQUESTS
& praise for answered prayers:

DIG DEEPER: how does it apply to my life?

GIVE THANKS
what I'm grateful for today:

REFLECTIONS & NOTES:

_____

_____

_____

_____

_____

_____

_____

_____

_____

_____

_____

_____

_____

_____

_____

_____

PRAY & WRITE TODAY'S VERSE:
Micah 5:2

STUDY NOTES: what does this scripture mean?

_____

_____

_____

_____

_____

_____

_____

_____

_____

_____

TODAY'S date: _____

PRAYER REQUESTS
& praise for answered prayers:

. . . .

. . . .

. . . .

. . . .

. . . .

. . . .

. . . .

. . . .

DIG DEEPER: how does it apply to my life?

_____

_____

_____

_____

_____

_____

_____

_____

GIVE THANKS
what I'm grateful for today:

. . . .

. . . .

. . . .

. . . .

. . . .

. . . .

. . . .

. . . .

REFLECTIONS & NOTES:

PRAY & WRITE TODAY'S VERSE:
Luke 2:8-11

STUDY NOTES: what does this scripture mean?

_____
_____
_____
_____
_____
_____
_____
_____
_____
_____
_____

DIG DEEPER: how does it apply to my life?

_____
_____
_____
_____
_____
_____
_____
_____
_____

TODAY'S date: _____

PRAYER REQUESTS
& praise for answered prayers:

....
....
....
....
....
....
....
....

GIVE THANKS
what I'm grateful for today:

....
....
....
....
....
....
....
....

REFLECTIONS & NOTES:

PRAY & WRITE TODAY'S VERSE:

Luke 2:12-16

STUDY NOTES: what does this scripture mean?

TODAY'S date: _____

_____

_____

_____

_____

_____

_____

_____

_____

_____

_____

PRAYER REQUESTS
& praise for answered prayers:

....

....

....

....

....

....

....

....

....

DIG DEEPER: how does it apply to my life?

_____

_____

_____

_____

_____

_____

_____

_____

GIVE THANKS
what I'm grateful for today:

....

....

....

....

....

....

....

....

REFLECTIONS & NOTES:

PRAY & WRITE TODAY'S VERSE:

Matthew 2:1-2

STUDY NOTES: what does this scripture mean?

_____
_____
_____
_____
_____
_____
_____
_____
_____
_____

DIG DEEPER: how does it apply to my life?

_____
_____
_____
_____
_____
_____
_____
_____

TODAY'S date: _____

PRAYER REQUESTS
& praise for answered prayers:

....
....
....
....
....
....
....
....

GIVE THANKS
what I'm grateful for today:

....
....
....
....
....
....
....
....

REFLECTIONS & NOTES:

PRAY & WRITE TODAY'S VERSE:
Matthew 2:10-11

STUDY NOTES: what does this scripture mean?

_____
_____
_____
_____
_____
_____
_____
_____
_____
_____
_____

DIG DEEPER: how does it apply to my life?

_____
_____
_____
_____
_____
_____
_____
_____
_____
_____

TODAY'S date: _____

PRAYER REQUESTS
& praise for answered prayers:

. . . .
. . . .
. . . .
. . . .
. . . .
. . . .
. . . .
. . . .
. . . .

GIVE THANKS
what I'm grateful for today:

. . . .
. . . .
. . . .
. . . .
. . . .
. . . .
. . . .
. . . .

REFLECTIONS & NOTES:

_____
_____
_____
_____
_____
_____
_____
_____
_____
_____

STUDY NOTES: what does this scripture mean?

TODAY'S date: _____

_____
_____
_____
_____
_____
_____
_____
_____
_____
_____

PRAYER REQUESTS
& praise for answered prayers:

....
....
....
....
....
....
....
....

DIG DEEPER: how does it apply to my life?

_____
_____
_____
_____
_____
_____
_____
_____

GIVE THANKS
what I'm grateful for today:

....
....
....
....
....
....
....
....

REFLECTIONS & NOTES:

_____

_____

_____

_____

_____

_____

_____

_____

_____

_____

_____

_____

_____

_____

_____

_____

_____

_____

PRAY & WRITE TODAY'S VERSE:

Matthew 2:16–18
& Jeremiah 31:15

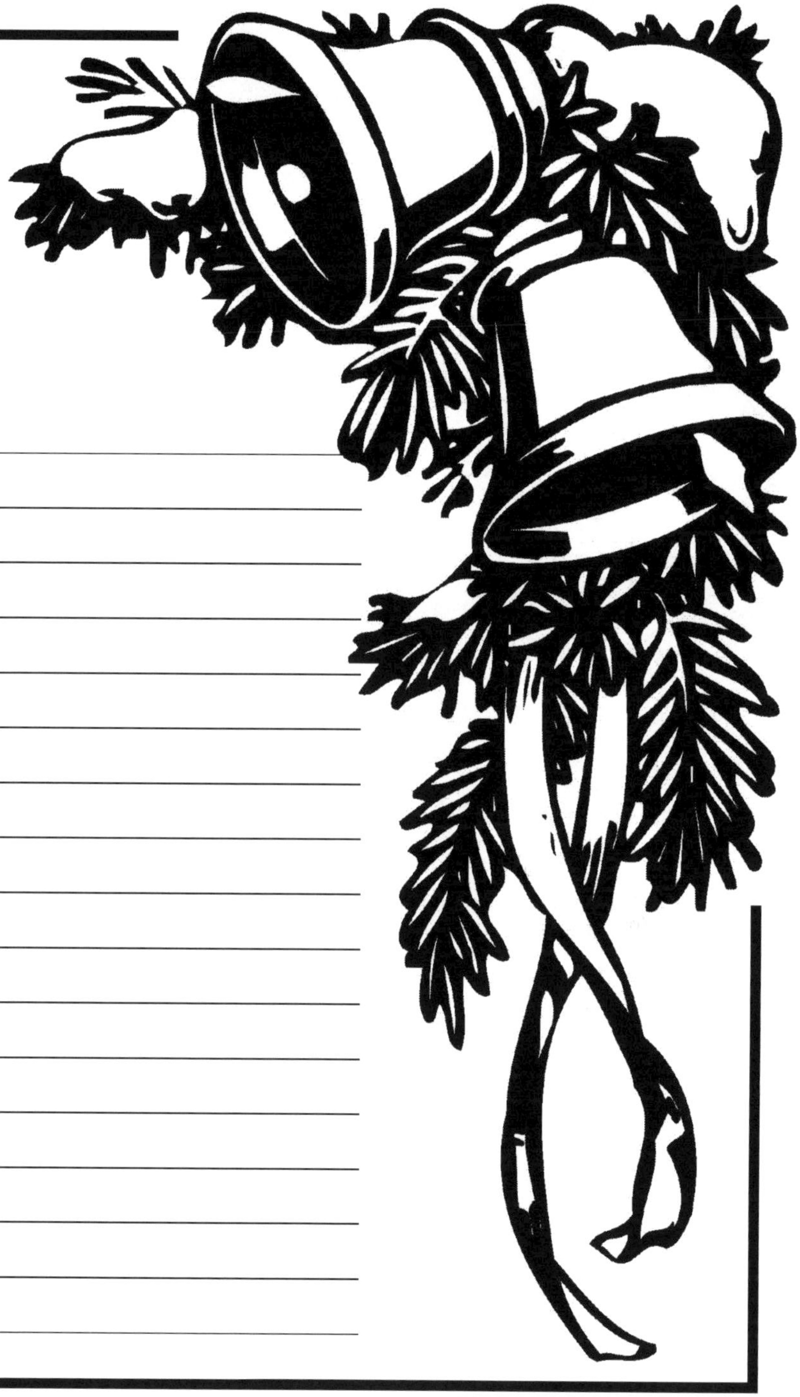

STUDY NOTES: what does this scripture mean?

_____
_____
_____
_____
_____
_____
_____
_____
_____
_____

DIG DEEPER: how does it apply to my life?

_____
_____
_____
_____
_____
_____
_____
_____

TODAY'S date: _____

PRAYER REQUESTS
& praise for answered prayers:

....
....
....
....
....
....
....
....

GIVE THANKS
what I'm grateful for today:

....
....
....
....
....
....
....
....

REFLECTIONS & NOTES:

PRAY & WRITE TODAY'S VERSE:
Matthew 2:19—23

STUDY NOTES: what does this scripture mean?

_____
_____
_____
_____
_____
_____
_____
_____
_____
_____
_____

DIG DEEPER: how does it apply to my life?

_____
_____
_____
_____
_____
_____
_____
_____
_____

TODAY'S date: _____

PRAYER REQUESTS
& praise for answered prayers:

....
....
....
....
....
....
....
....

GIVE THANKS
what I'm grateful for today:

....
....
....
....
....
....
....
....
....

REFLECTIONS & NOTES:

_____

_____

_____

_____

_____

_____

_____

_____

_____

_____

_____

_____

_____

_____

_____

_____

_____

_____

_____

_____

_____

_____

_____

_____

_____

_____

_____

_____

_____

PRAY & WRITE TODAY'S VERSE:

John 3:16—18

STUDY NOTES: what does this scripture mean?

_____
_____
_____
_____
_____
_____
_____
_____
_____
_____

DIG DEEPER: how does it apply to my life?

_____
_____
_____
_____
_____
_____
_____
_____

TODAY'S date: _____

PRAYER REQUESTS
& praise for answered prayers:

....
....
....
....
....
....
....
....
....

GIVE THANKS
what I'm grateful for today:

....
....
....
....
....
....
....
....
....

REFLECTIONS & NOTES:

Made in the USA
Middletown, DE
11 November 2023

42408873R00062